Pinocchio

retold by FREYA LITTLEDALE

from the original version: *THE ADVENTURES OF PINOCCHIO*
by C. COLLODI

with the original illustrations of ATTILIO MUSSINO

Cover painting by Ted Hanke

SCHOLASTIC BOOK SERVICES
NEW YORK · TORONTO · LONDON · AUCKLAND · SYDNEY · TOKYO

For Ann McGovern

0-590-12070-0

12 11 10 9 8 7 6 5 4 3 2   3 4 5 6 7/8

Printed in the U.S.A.   09

Pinocchio

Gepetto Makes a Puppet

Once upon a time, in a faraway land, there lived a poor old wood carver named Gepetto. He had no wife and he had no children. He lived alone with his cat.

One day a friend gave him a big piece of wood. Gepetto was very happy. "This is just right for a puppet," said he. "I will make a little boy and call him Pinocchio. He will be like a son to me."

And he set to work. First he made the hair, then the forehead, then the eyes. All at once the eyes began to move. "What's this!" cried Gepetto. "My puppet is alive!"

He carved the nose and it grew and grew. The more he cut it, the longer it grew.

And when he made the mouth, it began to laugh, "Ha, ha, ha!"

"Stop laughing!" said Gepetto. Well, the mouth stopped laughing, but it stuck out its tongue.

Gepetto pretended not to see, but he was very sad. "You're not even finished and you're giving me trouble," he thought. But he went on with his work until it was done. Then the puppet kicked him on the end of his nose.

"Shame on you!" said Gepetto. "That's no way to treat your father." He wiped a tear from his eye and took Pinocchio in his arms. Then he put him on the floor to teach him how to walk.

Pinocchio's legs were stiff at first. But it didn't take him long to move. It didn't take him long to walk. And it didn't take him long to run out the door and into the street.

"Stop him!" shouted Gepetto. But no one did. So away ran Pinocchio with Gepetto running after him. At last a policeman caught Pinocchio by the nose and held him for Gepetto.

"Bad boy!" said Gepetto. "I'll take care of you when we get home."

At these words, Pinocchio threw himself down in the middle of the street. He wouldn't move an inch. People stopped to see what was wrong, and they all had something to say.

"The puppet is very unhappy," said one.

"Gepetto must be a mean man," said another.

The people made so much noise, the policeman took poor Gepetto away and put him in jail for the night.

Pinocchio Meets the Talking Cricket

Meanwhile, Pinocchio found his way back home. He was so tired he lay down on the bed. Then all at once he heard a noise. "Cri-cri-cri!"

"Who's there?" called Pinocchio.

"It's I!"

Pinocchio looked up and saw a big cricket near the window. "Who are you?" he asked.

"I'm the Talking Cricket. I've lived in this room a long, long time."

"Go away," said Pinocchio. "This is my room now."

"No," said the Cricket. "I have to tell you something."

"Hurry up and tell me," said Pinocchio.

"You must never run away again. You'll be sorry if you don't listen to your father."

"Ho-hum," said Pinocchio. "You can talk all you want. But tomorrow I'm going to run away again. If I stay here, I'll be just like other boys. I'll have to go to school and learn. That's no fun. I want to play every day."

"Then you'll become a donkey," said the Cricket.

"Keep quiet!" said Pinocchio.

But the Cricket didn't keep quiet. "If you don't go to school, you must go to work."

"I'm going to have fun all the time," said Pinocchio.

"I feel sorry for you!" said the Cricket.

"Why?"

"Because you're a puppet with a wooden head."

Pinocchio was very angry. He was so angry he picked up a hammer and threw it at the Talking Cricket. Suddenly the Cricket was gone.

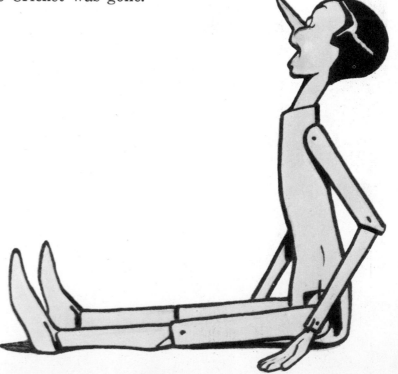

Pinocchio and the Egg

"I'm glad he's gone!" said Pinocchio. "Now I must find something to eat. I'm so hungry my stomach hurts."

He looked all over the house for food, but he found nothing. Then he began to cry. "The Talking Cricket was right! I wish I hadn't run away. I wish my father were here now. He would feed me."

Then Pinocchio saw something small and white in a pile of dust. It looked just like an egg. He ran and grabbed it. It *was* an egg.

He was so happy he kissed it and said, "Should I fry it? Should I scramble it? No! The quickest way is to cook it in water." So he put some water in a pan. When the water began to boil, he broke the shell. But instead of an egg, out popped a happy little chicken.

"Thank you very much," said the chicken. "I didn't have to break the shell myself." Then it spread its

wings and flew out the window. Pinocchio couldn't believe his eyes.

He felt so weak he lay down and fell asleep. But his feet were close to the stove, and little by little they burned to cinders. Pinocchio slept on as if his wooden feet belonged to someone else.

Just then the door opened and in came Gepetto. "Pinocchio!" he cried. "How did you burn your feet?"

"I don't know," said Pinocchio. "But I'll never walk again! And I'm dying of hunger!"

"There, there," said Gepetto. "Everything is going to be all right." And he gave Pinocchio three big pears. Pinocchio ate them up in six big bites.

Gepetto Sells His Coat

Pinocchio patted his stomach. "I feel better now," he said. "But I want new feet!"

"If I make new feet, you'll run away again."

"No, I won't," said Pinocchio.

"Don't say it if you don't mean it," said Gepetto.

"I *do* mean it," said Pinocchio. And he began to cry. "I promise I'll be good. I'll even go to school." And he cried so long, and he cried so hard, Gepetto set to work. And it wasn't long before the two little feet were finished.

"Thank you," said Pinocchio. "I will keep my promise and go to school. But first I need some clothes."

So Gepetto made him a suit and Pinocchio put it on at once. "Now I *could* go to school," he said, "if I had a spelling book."

"I have no money to buy one," said Gepetto. "But don't you worry. I'll find a way." And he put on his old coat and left the house.

He came back very soon — without his coat. In his hands was a fine new spelling book.

"Where's your coat?" asked Pinocchio.

"I sold it," said Gepetto.

"Why?" asked Pinocchio.

"It was too hot."

Pinocchio knew the truth. And he threw his arms around Gepetto and kissed him.

Pinocchio Sells His Spelling Book

The next morning Pinocchio set out for school with his spelling book. As he walked he said to himself, "Today I will learn to read. Tomorrow I will learn to write. And soon I will earn enough money to buy a new coat for my father. His coat will be made of gold. The buttons will be made of gold. And he'll have a gold hat to match."

All at once Pinocchio heard the beating of drums — boomety-boom. He heard the sound of a trumpet — tantara-tantara. They were the most wonderful sounds he had ever heard.

Then he saw a crowd of people in front of a beautiful building. Pinocchio ran toward the building. He ran to the middle of the crowd.

"What's going on?" Pinocchio asked a little boy.

"Read the sign," said the boy.

"I can't read," said Pinocchio.

"Donkey!" said the boy. "I'll read it to you. The sign says: COME AND SEE THE GREAT PUPPET SHOW. It costs ten pennies to get in."

"I can see the show today and go to school tomorrow," thought Pinocchio. "But I have no money." Then he turned to the boy. "Will you lend me ten pennies?"

"No," said the boy.

The drums went on beating. The trumpet went on playing, and the crowd was going inside. Pinocchio could hardly bear it. He *had* to see the show.

At last, with tears in his eyes, he said to the boy, "Will you . . . buy . . . my new spelling book?"

"No!" said the boy.

"I will," said a peddler who had been listening nearby. Then and there the fine new spelling book was sold.

Pinocchio bought a ticket and went inside. "Come up here!" called the other puppets. "You belong with us!"

Pinocchio jumped up on stage and the puppets hugged him like a brother.

Then out came the showman. His name was Fire-eater. He was big and ugly. His beard touched the floor and his eyes were like small, red lights. "You there!" He pointed to Pinocchio. "Go backstage! I'll take care of you later. The rest of you get on with the show!"

Pinocchio was very frightened and he ran backstage.

When the show was over,
Fire-eater said, "I'm roast-
ing a sheep for my supper. I need more wood for the
fire. You will do nicely."

"No!" screamed Pinocchio. "I don't want to die!"
And he cried and cried and cried.

Pinocchio Saves a Friend

Fire-eater sneezed loudly and the other puppets smiled. "That's good news," they whispered to Pinocchio. "He always sneezes when he feels sorry for someone. Now you have nothing to fear." But Pinocchio couldn't stop crying.

"*Please* stop that," said Fire-eater, "and tell me how you got here."

Pinocchio wiped his tears and told Fire-eater all about himself. He told him about his father who sold his coat for the spelling book.

"Your poor father would be sad if I threw you into the fire," said Fire-eater. "So I'll use another puppet instead."

The puppets shook with fright and Pinocchio began to cry again. "No! I won't let a friend die in my place. Come! Throw me into the flames!"

At these brave words, all the puppets began to cry. And Fire-eater couldn't stop sneezing.

"All right! All right!" he said at last. "I'll eat my sheep half-cooked. You may all go free!"

When they heard this, the puppets were so happy,
they danced together until dawn.

Pinocchio Meets the Fox and the Cat

The next day Fire-eater gave Pinocchio five gold coins for Gepetto. "Tell your father they're a gift from me," he said.

Pinocchio gave Fire-eater a big kiss on the end of his nose. Then he said good-bye to the other puppets and went on his way. He could hardly wait to give the gold to Gepetto.

He had not gone far when he saw a lame Fox and a blind Cat walking together like two good friends. "Hello, Pinocchio," said the Fox.

"How do you know my name?"

"I know your father," said the Fox. "I saw him just this morning. He was shivering with cold and calling your name."

"He won't be cold anymore," said Pinocchio. And he took the gold coins from his pocket. Quickly, the Cat opened her blind eyes and the Fox held out his lame paw. But Pinocchio didn't see them.

"What will you do with that money?" asked the Fox.

"First I'll buy a new coat for my father," said

Pinocchio. "Then I'll buy a spelling book for myself."

"You can do better than that," said the Fox.

"How?" asked Pinocchio.

"Come with us to the magic field," said the Fox.

"You plant gold coins in the earth, and the gold grows into a tree. The tree won't be covered with leaves. Oh no! Your tree will be covered with gold coins. All you have to do is to pick them."

"How many?" asked Pinocchio.

"Hundreds!" said the Cat.

"Thousands!" said the Fox. "Come on! Don't you want to get rich?"

Pinocchio thought for a while. "Yes I do," he said. "But I should go home now. My father is waiting for me."

"You'll be sorry," said the Fox. "Just think! Instead of five gold coins, you'll have a whole tree filled with gold."

"That would be wonderful!" said Pinocchio.

"Come with us then," said the Fox. "There's a fine inn nearby. We can stop and eat first. Then we'll go to the magic field."

"This is too good to miss," said Pinocchio. "I will go with you."

That very moment Pinocchio heard a voice say, "Don't go! They'll get you into trouble." Pinocchio knew it was the Talking Cricket and he didn't want to listen. So away he went.

Pinocchio at the Inn

They walked and walked and walked until they reached the inn. The Cat ate fifty sardines and the Fox ate ten chickens. Pinocchio had some soup.

When supper was over the Fox asked the innkeeper for two of his best rooms. "One is for the Cat and me," he said. "The other is for our good friend,

Pinocchio. A little sleep will do him good before we go. But be sure to wake us at midnight."

Pinocchio fell asleep as soon as he got into bed. He was dreaming about a tree of gold when there was a knock at the door. "It's midnight," called the innkeeper.

"Are my friends ready?" asked Pinocchio.

"The Cat's kitten was sick," said the innkeeper, "and they both left early. They want you to meet them at the magic field at sunrise."

"Did they pay you?" asked Pinocchio.

"Oh no," said the innkeeper. "They knew you would take care of that."

Pinocchio gave the innkeeper one of his gold coins and left.

It was very dark and he walked slowly along the road. All at once he heard a voice call, "Turn back!"

"Who's there?" asked Pinocchio.

"The Talking Cricket."

"You again!" said Pinocchio.

"Listen to me," said the Cricket. "Go home to your father now. Be careful of robbers."

"I don't need you to tell me anything," said Pinocchio. "Good night and good-bye."

Pinocchio and the Robbers

"It never ends," thought Pinocchio. "Everyone is always telling me what to do." And he walked more slowly than before.

Suddenly he heard footsteps. He turned and saw two figures right behind him. They wore sacks with holes for the eyes.

"Robbers!" thought Pinocchio. Quickly, he hid the coins in his mouth.

The robbers grabbed Pinocchio's arms. "Your money or your life!" they said. Pinocchio said nothing.

"If you don't give us your money, we'll kill you and your father!"

"Not my father!" said Pinocchio. And as he spoke, the coins jingled in his mouth.

"Now we know where the money is!" said the robbers. Then one of them grabbed Pinocchio's nose. The other pulled open his mouth. Pinocchio bit down as hard as he could. He bit right into a furry paw.

Then Pinocchio got free. He put the coins in his pocket and ran and ran and ran. The robbers were behind him. His heart pounded. He was out of breath, and he thought he couldn't go on. He climbed to the top of a tree and rested on a branch. The robbers waited below.

"We'll get you yet!" they shouted. Then they made a pile of dry wood and they set the wood on fire. The flames rose higher and higher and higher.

Pinocchio jumped down from the tree and ran through the woods. Soon he came to a wide stream and he leaped across it. The robbers leaped too, but they fell right into the water.

"Have a good bath!" shouted Pinocchio. He thought that was the end of them. But when he looked back, the robbers were still chasing him.

Pinocchio and the Fairy with Blue Hair

Pinocchio ran for miles with the robbers right behind him. He was weak and sick from running. He almost gave up but, suddenly, he came to a little house. A beautiful Fairy with blue hair stood at the door. "Come in," she said.

"Thank you," said Pinocchio. Then he fainted.

The Fairy put Pinocchio to bed and sent for the doctors. They were a Crow, an Owl, and the Talking Cricket.

"Is this puppet alive or dead?" asked the Fairy.

"He's almost alive," said the Owl.

"He's almost dead," said the Crow.

"He's a very bad puppet," said the Talking Cricket. Pinocchio opened his eyes and began to shake.

"He makes his father unhappy," said the Cricket. Pinocchio began to cry.

"He must be getting better," said the Owl.

"He must be getting worse," said the Crow.

"He hasn't changed a bit," said the Cricket. And all three doctors left the room.

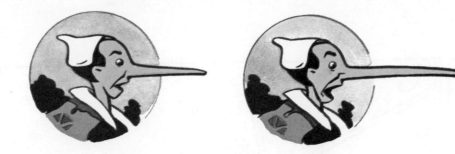

It was a long time before Pinocchio was well again. Then the good Fairy asked him about the robbers. And Pinocchio told her the whole story.

"Where are the gold coins now?" she asked.

"I lost them," said Pinocchio. But he was lying. They were still in his pocket. At once his nose began to grow.

"Where did you lose them?" asked the Fairy.

"In the woods," said Pinocchio. At this second lie, his nose grew even longer.

"No, I forgot," said Pinocchio. "I swallowed them when I bit the robber."

At this third lie, his nose grew so long Pinocchio could hardly move. His nose hit the ceiling, the walls, the window.... It almost hit the beautiful Fairy.

"You're lying," said the Fairy.

"Who told you?" asked Pinocchio.

"Your nose told me," said the Fairy.

Pinocchio wanted to hide. But he couldn't go anywhere with that nose.

Then he cried so hard the good Fairy felt sorry for him. She clapped her hands and hundreds of woodpeckers flew in through the window. They pecked at Pinocchio's nose until it was back to its usual size.

"Thank you," said Pinocchio. "You are a good Fairy and I will never forget you. Now I want to go home and see my father." And he kissed the Fairy good-bye and went on his way.

Pinocchio Meets the Fox
and the Cat Again

When he reached the woods he saw the Fox and the Cat. "Ah!" said the Fox. "Here is our good friend Pinocchio."

"What are you doing here?" asked the Cat.

"It's a long story," said Pinocchio. "I was almost robbed."

"Poor Pinocchio!" said the Cat. "Do you still have the gold?"

"Oh yes," said Pinocchio. "I have four coins left."

"Good," said the Fox. "Then it's not too late to go to the magic field."

As they were talking, Pinocchio saw that the Cat's paw was hurt. "What happened to your paw?" he asked.

"It was bitten by a hungry mouse," said the Cat. "But I don't blame him. The poor thing was half-starved."

"How kind you are," said Pinocchio.

"And I want to be kind to you too, Pinocchio," said

the Cat. "I want to take you to the magic field."

"We'll go another time," said Pinocchio.

"No," said the Fox. "This is your last chance. The field will be closed tomorrow."

Pinocchio didn't know what to do. He wanted to see his father and he wanted to get rich. At last he said, "How far is it to the field?"

"Only an hour away," said the Fox. "Just plant the money, pluck the coins from the tree, and go home to your father."

"That shouldn't take long," said Pinocchio.

"I'll do it."

Pinocchio Goes to the Magic Field

They walked for three hours until they reached the magic field. It looked just like any other field. "Is this it?" asked Pinocchio.

"This is it," said the Fox. "Now dig a hole, plant the gold, and give it a little water."

Pinocchio did as he was told. Then, since he had no watering can, he took off his shoe and filled it with water from a nearby stream. Carefully, he poured the water over the earth.

"Is that all?" he asked.

"That's all," said the Fox. "Now leave the field and don't look back. Return in twenty minutes and you'll be rich."

Pinocchio didn't know how to thank them. "I will buy you each a beautiful gift," he said.

"We don't want gifts," said the Fox and the Cat. "It makes us happy just to help you." And they said good-bye and left.

Twenty minutes seemed like twenty days to Pinocchio. He walked this way and that way. He could almost see that tree with a thousand gold coins.

What a fine gentleman he would be! He'd build a beautiful house. No! He'd build a beautiful *palace*. He could hardly wait.

When he thought the time was up, he walked back to the field. He looked for the tree of gold. But he saw nothing. He waited. Maybe he needed a few more minutes. Still he saw nothing. He moved up to the spot where the gold was buried...nothing. He dug deep down in the earth...nothing. His four gold coins were gone!

Then he saw a Parrot and he heard him laugh. "What's so funny?" asked Pinocchio.

"You are!" said the Parrot. How could you believe those robbers? When you left the field, the Cat and Fox came back. They took your money and ran."

"No!" cried Pinocchio.

"Yes!" said the Parrot.

"I'll catch them!" said Pinocchio.

"Never!" said the Parrot.

Pinocchio Flies to the Seashore

As Pinocchio left the field, he thought how bad and foolish he had been. But he was going to change and make his father happy.

Suddenly, he saw a large Pigeon flying toward him. "Do you know a puppet called Pinocchio?" asked the Pigeon.

"I am Pinocchio!"

At once the Pigeon flew to the ground. "Do you know Gepetto?"

"He's my father!" said Pinocchio. "Have you seen him?"

"I saw him at the seashore," said the Pigeon. "He has been looking high and low for you. Come! Hop on my back and we'll fly to the shore."

"Thank you," said Pinocchio. And he hopped on the Pigeon's back and flew way up in the air. They flew for hours and hours and at last they reached the seashore.

It was crowded with people. They were shouting,
"Poor man! He can't swim!"

"What's happening?" asked Pinocchio.

"A man has been looking everywhere for his son," said an old woman. "He made a boat to cross the ocean and find him. But a storm is coming and the waves are high. The boat is going to sink!"

Pinocchio climbed on top of a high rock. He saw the little man in the little boat. "Papa!" he cried.

"Pinocchio!" called the old man.

Then a great wave came and the boat was gone. "I must save him!" shouted Pinocchio. And he jumped into the sea.

It rained all through the night. The thunder was as loud as cannons. Lightning lit up the sky. Pinocchio swam and swam, but he couldn't find his father.

The Village of the Busy Bees

In the morning he saw an island and a big wave threw him on shore. Soon the sun came out and the sea was as smooth as glass. Pinocchio looked for his father in the little boat. But he saw nothing. Only a Dolphin was swimming nearby.

"Hello, fish," said Pinocchio. "Do you know where I can get some food?"

"Follow the road behind you," said the Dolphin.

"Please tell me something else," said Pinocchio.

"I'll tell you anything I know," said the Dolphin.

"Have you seen a little boat with my father in it?"

"No," said the Dolphin. "But I've seen a terrible Shark."

"I hope the Shark didn't see my father," said Pinocchio.

"I hope not," said the Dolphin. And he swam away.

Pinocchio took the road behind him and he reached the Village of the Busy Bees. Everywhere he looked, people were working.

"This is not the place for me," said Pinocchio.

"I hate to work. I'm so hungry I'll have to beg for food."

Just then a man came along. He was carrying two boxes of wood. "Will you give me money for food?" asked Pinocchio.

"Yes," said the man, "if you help me carry this wood."

"No," said Pinocchio. "Work is not for me." So the man went on his way.

Soon an old farmer passed by. He was pulling a cart filled with hay.

"Will you give me money for food?" asked Pinocchio.

"Yes," said the farmer, "if you help me pull this cart."

"No," said Pinocchio. "Work is not for me." So the farmer went on his way.

Pinocchio asked everyone he saw. And everyone told him to work for his money.

At last a lady walked by. She wore a shawl on her head and she carried two pails of water. "Can I please have some water?" asked Pinocchio.

"Yes," said the lady.

Pinocchio drank and drank. "I'm not thirsty now," he said. "But I'm still hungry."

"If you carry this pail of water, I'll give you some bread," said the lady.

"I don't know...." said Pinocchio.

"With the bread I'll give you stew. And after the stew, I'll give you chocolate cake."

"I'll do it," said Pinocchio. And he carried the pail to the lady's house.

He ate the bread. He ate the stew, and he ate the cake. Then he patted his stomach and looked up.

"Oh!" he cried. "You're the Fairy with blue hair!" And he ran to kiss her.

Pinocchio Goes to School

Pinocchio told the Fairy all that had happened to him. "I'm so tired of being a puppet," he said. "I wish I were a real boy!"

"Your wish can come true," said the Fairy. "First you must be good and go to school and work hard."

"I'll try," said Pinocchio. "But will I ever see my father again?"

"I think you will," said the Fairy. "But tomorrow you must go to school."

"All right," said Pinocchio. "I'll do *anything* to become a real boy."

The next morning Pinocchio went to school. The children made fun of him. They pulled his nose. They tried to put strings on his hands and feet.

At first Pinocchio said nothing. But they kept on teasing. Then Pinocchio got so angry he kicked one of the boys with all his might. "Ouch!" screamed the boy. "What hard feet you have!" And he never teased Pinocchio again. No one did. Indeed, they soon made friends with him.

Pinocchio did well in school. But there was one problem. Some of his friends were always getting into trouble. The worst one of all was Candlewick. He was the laziest boy in school.

"Watch out for Candlewick," the Fairy warned him. "He can get you into trouble too."

"Don't worry about me," said Pinocchio, and he promised to be good and work hard.

Pinocchio kept his promise for almost a whole year. The Fairy was very pleased. And one day she said, "Tomorrow your wish will come true. You will become a real boy! We'll have a party and you can invite all your friends."

Pinocchio had never been so happy. "I can't wait until tomorrow," he said. "Can I go and invite them now?"

"Yes," said the Fairy. "But you must come home before dark."

"I'll be back in an hour," said Pinocchio. And off he went.

The Land of Play

In less than an hour, Pinocchio invited all his friends but one. He couldn't find Candlewick. At last he saw him hiding behind a big tree. "Candlewick!" he called. "Come to my party tomorrow. I'm going to become a real boy just like you!"

"I'll be gone tomorrow," said Candlewick. "Tonight I'm going to the most wonderful place in the world. It's called the Land of Play. There are no schools. There are no books. There are no teachers. Every day is a holiday."

"What do they do there?" asked Pinocchio.

"They play all day long," said Candlewick.

"It sounds wonderful!" said Pinocchio.

"Why don't you come with me?" asked Candlewick.

"Oh no!" said Pinocchio. "I have to go home."

"Wait until the coach comes," said Candlewick.

"I can't! I'm late already," said Pinocchio. "But tell me. Isn't there one school in the Land of Play?"

"Not one!" said Candlewick.

Just then the coach arrived. It was drawn by twenty-four donkeys. They all wore white boots.

Candlewick climbed into the coach that was filled with boys. "Come with me!" he called.

"Come with us!" shouted all the boys in the coach.

"No!" said Pinocchio. "I'm going home." But he didn't move.

"This is your last chance to play all the time!" said Candlewick.

The coach started to leave. In an instant, Pinocchio forgot his promise. He forgot everything but the Land of Play. "Stop!" he shouted. "I'm coming! I am!"

"There's no more room inside," said the Coachman. "But you can ride on one of the donkeys."

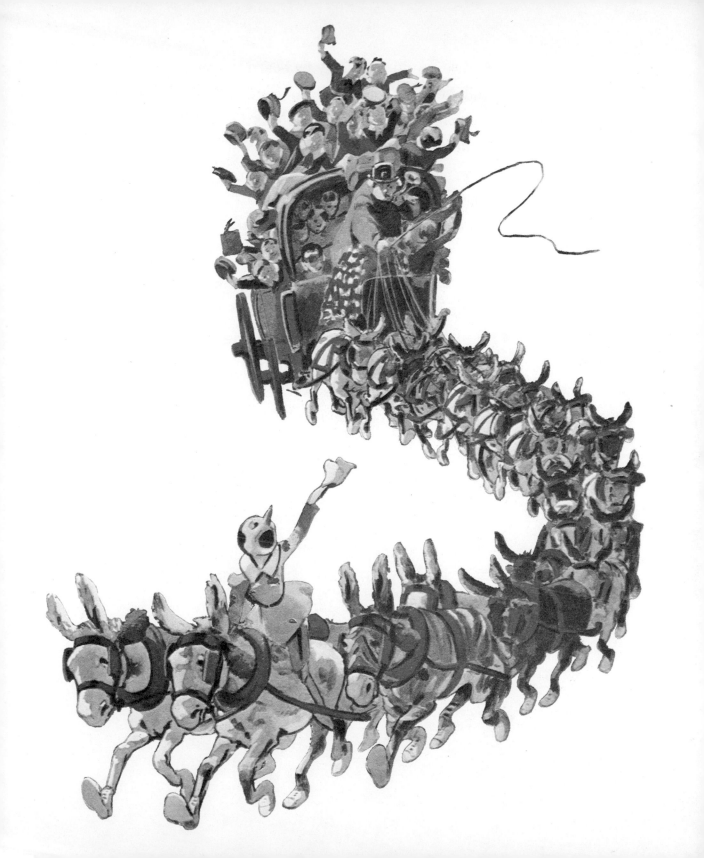

And so he did. Suddenly he heard the donkey speak. "You'll be sorry for this. Soon you'll cry just like me."

Pinocchio jumped off. "Mr. Coachman," he called, "this donkey is crying!"

"Don't listen," said the Coachman. "Climb back up and let's be off."

Pinocchio did as he was told. And by morning they were in the Land of Play.

Everyone was having a wonderful time. They were laughing and singing and running and shouting. Some were playing ball. Others were playing hide-and-seek. A few were on swings and many were playing tag. On the doors of the houses were signs: DOWN WITH SCHOOLS, DOWN WITH BOOKS, LONG LIVE THE LAND OF PLAY.

Pinocchio was happy from the moment he arrived. The time passed quickly. There were games and shows every hour of every day.

"What a wonderful life!" said Pinocchio.

"You owe it all to me!" said Candlewick.

"That's true," said Pinocchio. "You're my very best friend!"

This happy life went on for five months. But one morning Pinocchio woke up and he wasn't happy at all.

Pinocchio Becomes a Donkey

He had grown two long donkey's ears overnight. "This is horrible!" he cried. "I must tell Candlewick."

Pinocchio put on a big hat to cover his ears. Then he went to Candlewick's house. Candlewick was wearing a big hat too. "Let me see your ears," said Pinocchio.

"Let's see yours first," said Candlewick.

"No," said Pinocchio. "We'll take off our hats at the same time. One, two, three — hats off!"

They looked at each other's ears and laughed and laughed and laughed. Suddenly Candlewick yelled, "Help! I can't stand up!"

"I can't either!" cried Pinocchio.

Their hands and feet turned to hoofs. They both grew tails. They couldn't even cry like people. They could only bray like donkeys — because that's just what they were.

At that very moment the Coachman came in. "What fine donkeys you are," said he. He patted them and combed them. Then he put a halter around their necks and led them to market. "I will get a good price for you both," he said. And he was right.

Pinocchio in the Circus

Candlewick was sold to a farmer. Pinocchio was sold to the ringmaster of a circus who was going to teach him tricks.

It was a hard life. Pinocchio was given little food and many whippings. After three months he was ready for his first big show.

The tent was crowded with people who had come to see the famous donkey, Pinocchio. He had flowers behind his ears and bows on his tail. The people clapped when they saw him.

The ringmaster cracked his whip and said, "Bow, Pinocchio." Pinocchio bowed. "Now gallop!" said the ringmaster. Pinocchio galloped. "Faster!" he ordered. Pinocchio galloped around and around as fast as he could go.

Then the ringmaster fired a toy pistol. The little donkey fell down as if he were hurt. When he got up, the people shouted and applauded. Pinocchio bowed again.

Suddenly, right in the front seat, he saw the Fairy with blue hair. He tried to call out to her, but all he could do was bray.

"Stop that noise!" said the ringmaster. And he hit the donkey hard on his head. Pinocchio didn't dare make a sound. He closed his eyes with pain. But when he opened them, the Fairy was gone. Pinocchio began to weep. "I'll never see her again!" he thought. "Never!"

The ringmaster cracked his whip. "Now jump through the hoops!" he ordered. Pinocchio tried and tried. But each time he came to a hoop, he went around it. "Do what you're told, donkey!" yelled the ringmaster.

At last Pinocchio went through. But he caught his leg in one of the hoops and fell on the floor. He could hardly walk back to the stable.

"Bring back the little donkey, Pinocchio!" everyone shouted. But the little donkey was never seen again at the circus.

Pinocchio and the Drummer

The next morning the animal doctor looked at Pinocchio's leg. "Your donkey will be lame for the rest of his life," said the doctor.

"What good is a lame donkey to me?" said the ringmaster. "I will sell him."

So he took Pinocchio to the market and sold him to a drummer who played in the village band. "This donkey's skin is very hard," said the drummer. "It's just right for a drum."

He led Pinocchio to the seashore. Then he tied a rope around his leg and dropped him into the water. After an hour, he began to pull him out. "The poor donkey must be dead by now," he said. "And I will make my drum."

He pulled and pulled. But instead of a donkey — up came a live puppet.

"Who are you?" asked the drummer.

"I'm the donkey you threw into the sea."

"I don't believe it," said the drummer.

"Untie my leg and I'll tell you the whole story," said Pinocchio.

So the drummer untied his leg, and Pinocchio told him everything.

"But how can a donkey turn into a puppet?" asked the drummer.

"I think the good Fairy did that," said Pinocchio. She is like a mother to me. When she thought I might drown, she sent fish to eat me. But they didn't hurt at all. They ate the donkey and left the wood."

"Well, puppet," said the drummer, "I'll take you back to the market and sell you for wood."

"Oh no you won't!" said Pinocchio. And he jumped into the sea and swam away.

The Terrible Shark

Suddenly he saw a giant Shark. The Shark came toward him with his mouth wide open. Pinocchio was a good swimmer. But the Shark was better. There was no escape! The Shark opened his mouth wider and wider. Then he swallowed Pinocchio whole.

It was as dark as night inside the Shark. Pinocchio tried to be brave. But soon he began to cry, "Help! Save me!"

"I wish I could," said a voice.

"Who's that?" cried Pinocchio.

"I'm a tuna fish. They call me Tunny. The Shark swallowed me too."

As they were talking, Pinocchio saw a light way down inside the Shark. "What's that light?" he asked.

"Maybe it's the Shark's lunch," said Tunny.

"I'll go and see," said Pinocchio. "It might help us escape."

He moved slowly toward the light. It grew brighter and brighter with each step. And then he saw a little old man eating at a table lit by one candle. The little old man was Gepetto!

Pinocchio wanted to laugh and cry at the same time. "Dear Papa, I found you! I will never leave you again!" And he hugged and kissed the old man.

Gepetto couldn't believe his eyes. "Are you really my Pinocchio?"

"Yes, I am! Do you forgive me for all I've done? If only you knew all the terrible things that have happened!"

"Tell me," said Gepetto.

And Pinocchio did. When his story was finished, Gepetto's eyes filled with tears. "My poor boy!" he said.

"What about you, Papa?" asked Pinocchio. "How long have you been here?"

"Since the day of the storm," said Gepetto. "That was two long years ago!"

"How have you lived?" asked Pinocchio.

"There was a shipwreck that night," said Gepetto. "The Shark was still hungry. He swallowed everything on the ship — canned meats, cheeses, jams, dried fruit — enough for two years. There were also candles and matches. But this is the last candle. When it goes out, we'll both be in the dark."

"No we won't," said Pinocchio. "We'll escape the way we came in — through the Shark's mouth. Then we'll swim away."

"I can't swim," said Gepetto.

"I'll carry you," said Pinocchio. "Follow me." Then he picked up the candle and led the way.

The Shark was asleep with his mouth open. "Now!" whispered Pinocchio. They tiptoed across the Shark's tongue. Then, with Gepetto on his shoulders, Pinocchio dived into the sea.

Pinocchio Becomes a Real Boy

He swam and he swam and he swam. It was hard for Gepetto to hold on. "We'll reach shore soon," Pinocchio told him. But he really didn't see the shore. He was getting very tired.

Then, when he thought he could swim no more, he heard a voice. "Remember me, I'm Tunny. You showed me how to escape from the Shark."

"Oh Tunny, you came at the right time," said Pinocchio. "Help us or we'll drown!"

"Climb on my back," said Tunny. "I'll take you to shore as fast as I can."

And that's just what he did.

"Thank you, good friend," said Pinocchio.

"You're welcome," said Tunny. And he swam away.

Gepetto was so weak he could hardly walk. "Hold my arm," said Pinocchio. "We'll find a place to eat and rest."

They had not gone far when they saw the Fox and the Cat. But they looked different. The Cat was really blind and the Fox was really lame.

"You must help us," said the Fox.

"Go away," said Pinocchio. "You can't fool me any more."

"Believe me, we really need help," said the Cat.

"If that's true, I'm sorry for you," said Pinocchio. And he and Gepetto went on their way.

Soon they came to a little house. The door was open so they went inside. "Who lives here?" called Pinocchio.

"I do," said a voice from the ceiling.

They looked up and saw the Talking Cricket. "I'm glad to see you again," said Pinocchio.

"Now you're glad!" said the Cricket. "Once you threw a hammer at me!"

"You're right to be angry," said Pinocchio. "But please help my father. Tell me where I can get milk for him."

"Go to the farmer down the road," said the Cricket.

Pinocchio ran to the farmer and asked for one cup of milk. "That will cost two pennies," said the farmer.

"I don't have any money," said Pinocchio.

"If you don't have money, I don't have milk," said the farmer.

Pinocchio started to leave. "Wait," called the farmer. "If you work for me, I'll give you milk."

"What kind of work?" asked Pinocchio.

"Pump water from my well," said the Farmer. "I'll give you one quart of milk for one hundred buckets of water."

"I'll do it," said Pinocchio.

Pinocchio had never worked so hard in his life. The farmer was pleased. "Until now, this work was done by my donkey," he said. "But the animal is dying."

"May I see your donkey?" asked Pinocchio.

"Yes," said the farmer. And they went to the stable where a pretty little donkey was lying on the straw.

"I think I know this donkey," said Pinocchio. And he bent over the animal and whispered, "Candlewick?"

The donkey opened his eyes and looked at Pinocchio. He moved his head as if to say yes. Then he closed his eyes and died.

"My poor friend," said Pinocchio.

The farmer laughed. "How can a donkey be a friend?" Pinocchio said nothing. He went back to work.

From that day on, Pinocchio got up at sunrise. He pumped water for the farmer and got milk for his father. He even learned to make fine straw baskets which he sold at the market. He earned money to buy everything his father needed. And soon he had enough left over to buy a new coat for himself.

He was on his way to the store when the Talking Cricket called him. "Pinocchio, do you remember the Fairy with blue hair?"

"I'll never forget her," said Pinocchio. "Do you know where she is?"

"She's in the hospital," said the Cricket. "She's very sick and she has no money for food."

"Give her this money," said Pinocchio. "I was saving it for a coat, but maybe it will help."

"What about your coat?" asked the Cricket.

"The Fairy is more important than a coat," said Pinocchio. "She was like a mother to me."

That night Pinocchio stayed up very late. He made many straw baskets to sell at the market. Then, when he fell asleep, he had a dream. The Fairy kissed him and said, "Pinocchio, I forgive you for all you have done in the past."

In the morning Pinocchio awoke to a big surprise. He was no longer a puppet. At last he was a real boy!

And when he got out of bed, he found a new suit of clothes. He dressed quickly and put his hands in his pockets. There was a little purse and a note. "The Fairy returns the money to her dear Pinocchio and thanks him for his good heart." He opened the purse and, instead of forty pennies, he found forty gold coins.

"Papa!" he called, and he ran into the next room. Gepetto was no longer weak and sick. He was happy and well. He was busy carving birds and flowers out of wood.

"Look! Look at me!" he cried. "I am a real boy! What happened to the wooden puppet, Pinocchio?"

"He's over there," answered Gepetto. Then Pinocchio saw a big puppet lying across a chair.

"How silly I was when I was a puppet," he said. "And how happy I am to be a real boy!"